www.pixelmousehousebooks.com
www.bigbadcoronavirus.com

Pixel Mouse House publishes children variety books.

Updated Edition

ISBN 978-1-939322-36-4
Created in the U.S.A.

THE BIG BAD CORONA! VIRUS

And How We Can Beat It!

Written by Lisa Carroll   Drawn by G.F. Newland

LET'S ALL LEARN THE SAFETY RULES!

KIDS VS. COVID-19

Listen to the Health Experts

WASH YOUR HANDS OFTEN!

6 FEET APART

LEARN TO BE SAFE

Wear A Mask

It's the first day of school
and Lisa is afraid to go...

Lisa takes the bus to school,
like she did last year.

This year, kids are not
allowed to sit together.

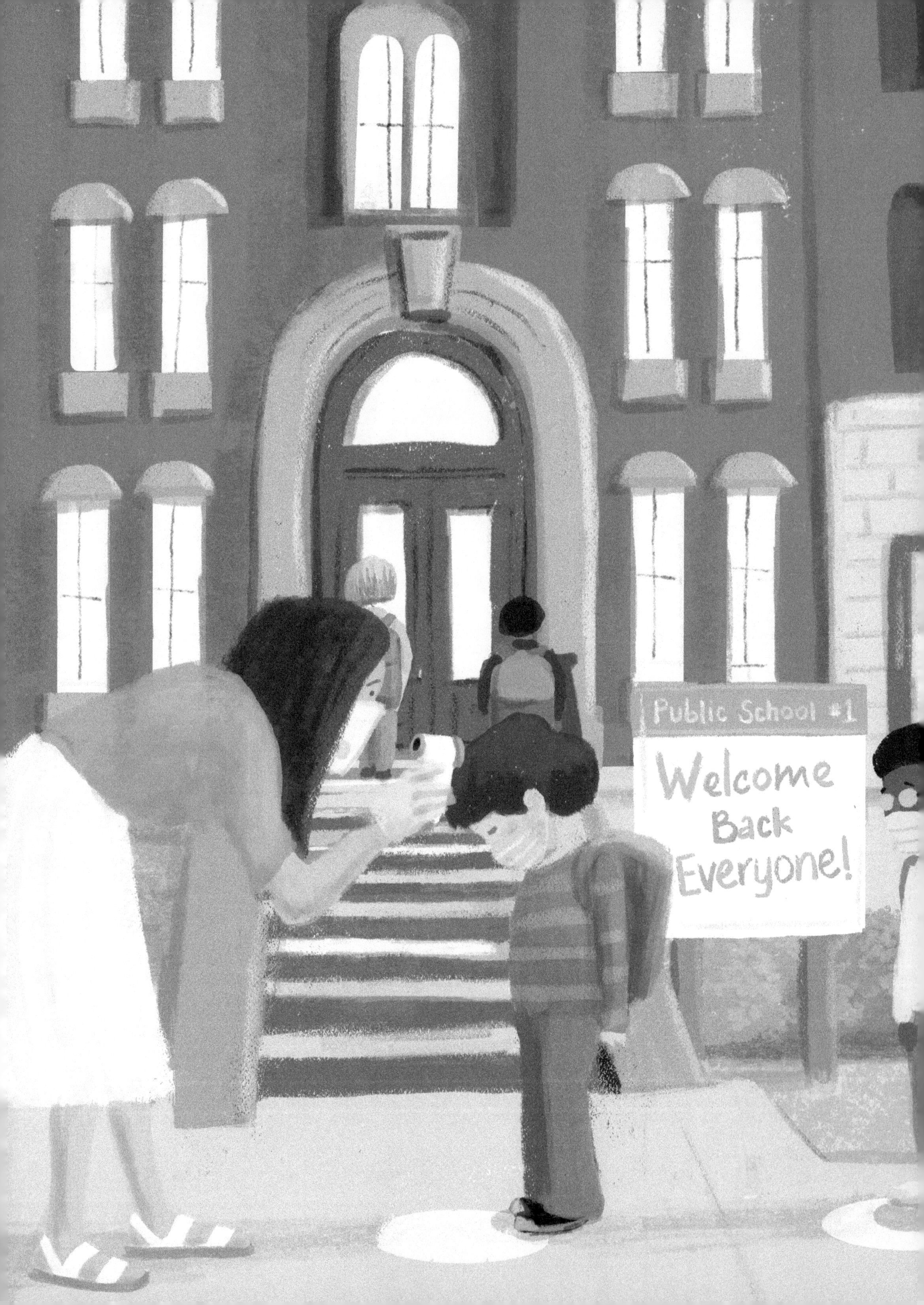
Public School #1
Welcome Back Everyone!

Lisa had to wait in line to be checked by the nurse.

During morning exercise,
she stayed in her marked-off spot.

Lisa's classroom looked the same,
but there were see-through boxes
on the desks.

There were new
signs on the wall.

Lisa noticed that
her best friend
Alfie wasn't in his
usual seat.

At lunch break, she
called him to ask why
he wasn't in class.

Alfie said he was Remote Learning from home because of the Big Bad Coronavirus.

"It's big, it's bad, and it flies through the air, making people sick!"

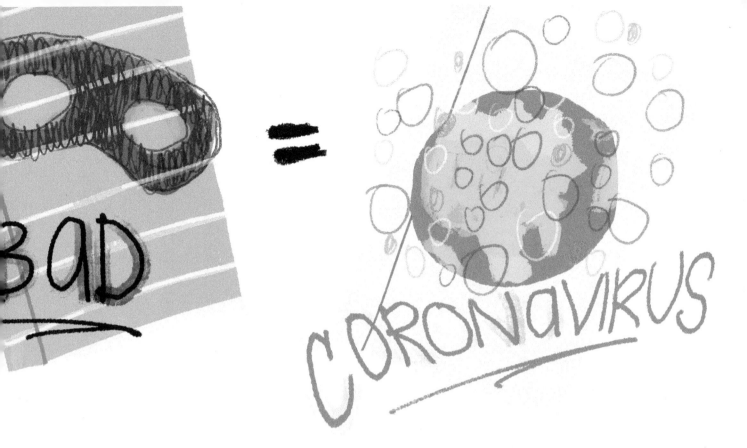

Lisa couldn't pay attention in math class, she doodled nervously in her notebook. All she could think about was Alfie and the Big Bad Coronavirus.

She was more scared now than ever! "There must be something we can do," she thought.

When Lisa got home,
she was so exhausted from worry
even her best pal, Hip Hop Hamilton,
didn't get a hug.

Instead, she took a nap
and had a scary dream.

The BIG BAD CORONAVIRUS!
She cried, and called her mommy.

MOMMY, I'M

WHY DO I HAVE TO WEAR A MASK?

WHY CAN'T ALFIE COME OVER?

WILL I GET SICK MOMMY?

WHAT IS COVID-19?

SCARED!

→ I'm afraid to go to school!

WHAT DOES ANTIBODIES MEAN?

→ Will You Get Sick, Mommy?

HOW MUCH IS SIX FEET?

What is the CORONAVIRUS?

Mommy saw how upset she was, and told her she could do Remote Learning, just like Alfie.

But first she had to learn all about the Big Bad Coronavirus.

Lisa, Mommy, and
Hip Hop Hamilton
searched the internet.

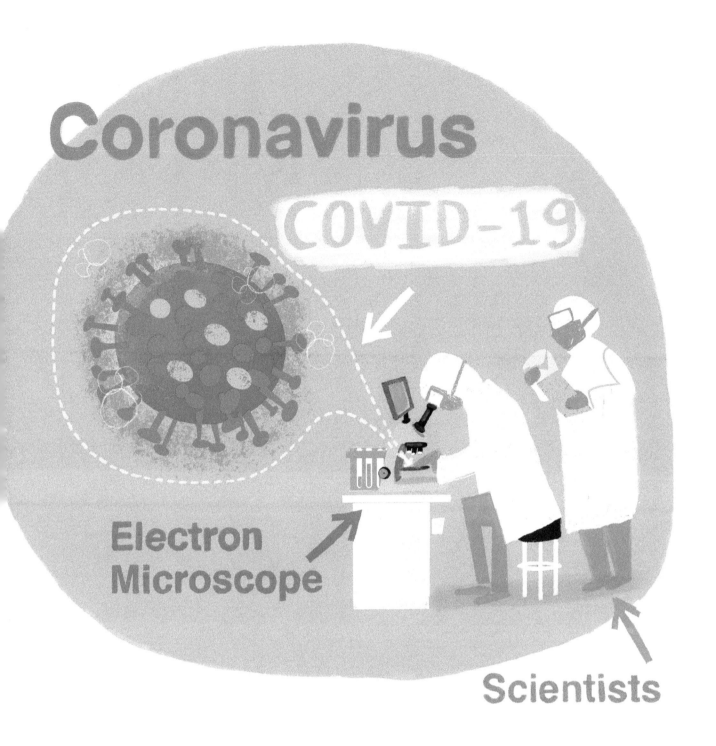

They saw pictures of scientists
looking at the Coronavirus
under a microscope.

Lisa learned about all
the ways you can catch
the Coronavirus.

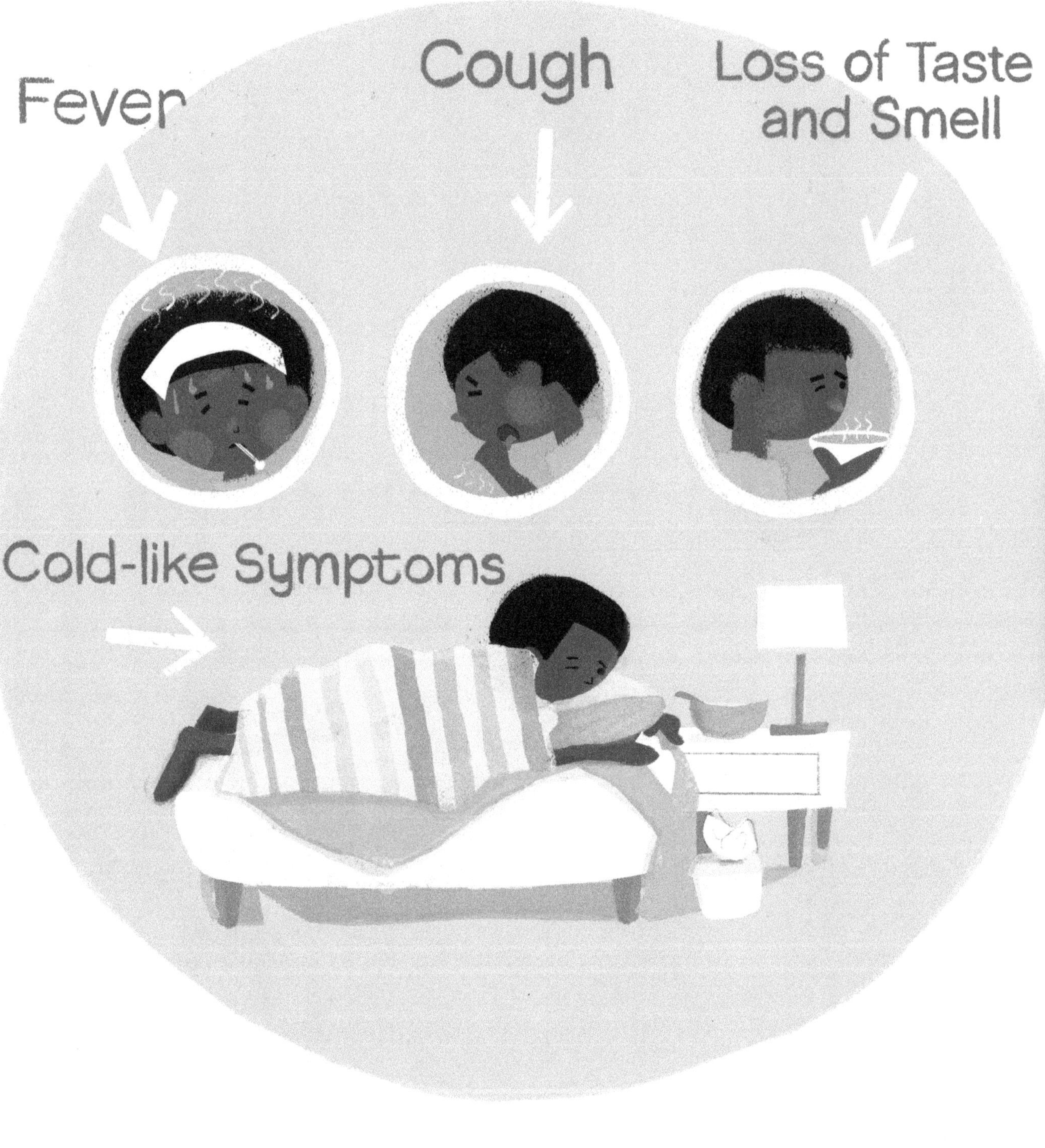

Fever

Cough

Loss of Taste and Smell

Cold-like Symptoms

Or No Symptoms at all!

Lisa learned what it feels like when you get sick.

"Remember when Alfie had the flu?" Mommy asked, "It's sort of like that, only much more serious. The good news is Doctors have already created vaccines to protect us. We just need to be careful and to look out for one another."

Mommy showed Lisa
the four things we can do to
avoid getting sick.

When You Go Out ...

Wear a Mask

6 Feet Apart

Use Hand Sanitizer

When You Get Home ...

SOAP

Wash your Hands

"Just like the
signs at school!"
Lisa said.

Lisa now knows that even though the Coronavirus is BIG and BAD...

These are the ways to stay safe,
and Lisa is not so afraid anymore.

The next day, Lisa begins
Remote Learning. Her
teacher gives an assignment:

"Students, draw a picture of
all the ways we can stay safe."

Lisa knows just what to do!

Lisa and Alfie work together on a drawing of the Big Bad Coronavirus!

They want to show their friends how to stay safe by following these basic rules;

Wear a Mask!

Stand six feet apart!

Use Hand Sanitizer
when you're out and about.

If you're not feeling well
or have a slight fever,
stay home.

Wash your hands a lot,
toss out used paper masks
or wash the cloth ones—like the
red polka dot mask Lisa wears.

Mommy says the drawing she and Alfie did is wonderful, and she's really proud that her daughter has learned so much.

"If we all follow the rules, we'll beat that Big Bad Coronavirus!"

She danced with Hip Hop Hamilton. Following the rules and staying safe makes Lisa very, very happy!

Scrub-a-dub-dub,
My hands in the tub,
I'm washin' all the germs away.
That Big Bad Virus
has already shown us
he's serious, not out to play.
So let's Scrub-a-dub
Scrub-a-dub-dub
Scrub-a-dub
Scrub-a-dub
Scrub-a-dub-a-dub-dub.
Twenty seconds is all it takes,
so wash your hands
for goodness' sakes!

Author Lisa Carroll is multi-talented: she acts, sings, writes, composes, and stays on top of marketing trends in the entertainment industry.

She is best known for her performance as Dolly Levi in the hit musical "Hello, Dolly." She acted as a stand in for star Carol Channing and appeared in numerous episodic television shows including General Hospital. Her most recent TV appearance was on ABC's "The Toy Box." Lisa's toys were a big hit with the panel of children judges.

Lisa travelled the world performing her one-woman show to universal acclaim: London's Daily Mirror reported that she "...took London's Cabaret scene by storm," and former Los Angeles Times critic, Charles Champlin, called her "...a singer and actress in one, with a large multi-colored voice."

As a writer and lyricist, Lisa honed her scripting skills for various PBS programs, and created and produced a children's Christmas Rap album for Capital Records', "Rappin Up Christmas." The success of this album led Lisa to develop (for the prestigious toy company, Gund, and others) a series of "animated," singing stuffed animals. These plushies, including Hip Hop Hamilton, are both educational and fun.

Through all her work, Lisa hopes to deliver the message to children that one can look awesome, be cool, and lead a life that reflects positive qualities. The Big Bad Coronavirus is her first children's book.

Hip Hop Hamilton
PLUSH BEAR
EXCLUSIVE OFFER!

For more information
send request to
info@pixelmousehouse.com

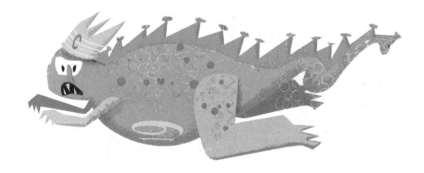

Illustrator G.F. Newland is average build in most things. He works at the School of Visual Arts by day, and in the evenings, he plays a variety of musical instruments in a couple of bands.

He's married, has a few grown kids, and lives somewhere in the middle of Brooklyn, where he's mostly happy a lot of the time.

He has illustrated 2 books for Pixel Mouse House/ Schiffer Kids: Sticks 'N Stones 'N Dinosaur Bones and The Bathysphere Boys.

For More Information
on the Coronavirus (Covid-19)
go to:
https://www.cdc.gov

CPSIA information can be obtained
at www.ICGtesting.com
Printed in the USA
BVHW020219290122
627538BV00005B/90